A True Story

You'll Know it When you See it

Nathaniel Frisby

WRITERS REPUBLIC L.L.C.
515 Summit Ave. Unit R1
Union City, NJ 07087, USA

Website: *www.writersrepublic.com*
Hotline: *1-877-656-6838*
Email: *info@writersrepublic.com*

Ordering Information:
Quantity sales. Special discounts are available on quantity purchases by corporations, associations, and others. For details, contact the publisher at the address above.

Library of Congress Control Number:		2023901273
ISBN-13:	979-8-88810-572-6	[Paperback Edition]
	979-8-88810-592-4	[Hardback Edition]
	979-8-88810-573-3	[Digital Edition]

Rev. date: 01/24/2023

CONTENTS

OPENING

When it comes to matters of the heart, I typically have a hard time trying to figure out who I want to give my love to. Over my 21 year journey, trying to figure out what the love I can offer could bring back to me, I realized love takes time to find the right two to make one. Being patience is an obstacle that we all face. Some days we're too eager to find love. So much so that we chase away the ones who are willing to love us for exactly who we are, leaving us empty hearted, alone and in a cloud of endless thoughts of "why does this keep happening to me?" And a handful of maybe. I think the older we get, the more susceptible to love we are. Think about it, when was the last time you came across someone who did take a piece of your heart with them when they walked out the door? Granted you gave it to them but still when was the last time? I think we as humans long for the feeling of another heart loving our own as if it was theirs too but some may never find that love they long for.

ACT 1

ME AND YOU

It all started with a hello. Feelings reciprocated, a connection brewing between us two, life was good. Your first name alone was enough for me to want to change your last name to mine, and with a feeling of running out of time, I needed to make you mine, so it all started with a hello. With your hi in return, it was more than enough to make my heart leap out of my chest, put love on my breath and had me drunk in love before contact was exchanged. The way your hair bounced when you walked had me captivated with disbelief that God would ever let an angle like you touch this earth. Your eyes pierced my soul when you looked at me. With a smile as contagious as yours, normally I could resist the urge but, I couldn't with you. You began to break my guard slowly. Your voice is the thing that would make my alarm clock collect dust if it sounded like you just to have me wake up and blow the dust off to do it all over again. The way your body leaned up against mine when we got close felt like you found comfort in my chest. Your hips, my favorite place to rest my hands after a long day of fighting, you became my refuge, and the way you walked right into my life made me believe I left the door open to the public but you protected my private things by closing the door on others that tried to follow in your footsteps when you came here and that lead me to trust you. Your aura trapped me into a place I never wanted to leave. A state of mind that felt safer than the one I know, my reality, and you alone became the one thing that made my heart beat a relaxing rhythm. Getting to know you felt effortless. Time invested every night to unlock stories that have yet to be told, my attention is on you. Dealing with my own temptation, to open my doors to those who knock, you remind me who you are and that keeps me focused on you.

12:53 and I'm thinking to myself, how long am I going to continue to allow myself to run wild, when I want to be tamed by the very flame that sparked my ambition? When will this longing for multiple subside for the one I want the most? When will my words speak just as loud as my actions, when it comes to the heart I want to place over mine, and when will I tell you how I really feel?

To the girl that knocks on my consciousness dubiously every night, I hope that one day, I can truthfully tell you about all the nights I spent lying awake daydreaming about the type of way I want to love you. The way I do in my dreams.

"Who do you see?"

Your attraction is what made me want to subtract the distance between us. There was no need for the unknown to stand in between you and I when knowing you is all I wanted to do. No problem would stand in my way when it came to knowing more than just your name. Your beauty, your name, your ambiance, it was just the tip of the iceberg that collided with fate. I had to get close to you. I had to know everything about you. Without knowing what's to come, I decided to take a leap of faith and hope to God that you would feel any amount of attraction towards me as I do you. You were something that seemed so far fetched but I was able to get one foot in the door, and that was all I needed to give you what I never knew I had inside of me. If I ever remember where your keys hide, knocking is only something I'll do when I want to surprise you with more of me. There are parts of me that you would've never thought you'd get to see from a guy in your entire life. Vulnerability and Stability are something most don't show but, as for me, I can confidently say, I do.

If you were a flower, I'd compare you to a rose.

Beautiful and elegant from afar but, to the touch, can hurt me, If not handled with care. However, if you let me, I'll hold you. I'll hold you just right with no reason to fight through the day and night because you know that I'm right here; Carefully observing the things that make you blossom but also taking heed, the things that make your thorns prick the hardest of skin, you've taken the heart of this man, and I don't understand but you've made it skip just for you.

Embellished by your conversation, captivated in your state of mind, you've placed me in a room of wonder

Like I wonder, if I pick you from this garden, plant you in mine, and take the time to refine all lies placed in your mind from the others that made you pluck petals, *he loves me he loves me not*, who would you believe?
The one who utters the right words just for you to be put in a Bouquet surrounded by others you don't even see or, the one that saw you as the most beautiful flower in the whole world. So beautiful that it enticed him to get close. Close enough to endure the pain that comes with holding something so beautiful that he picked you just so you could be set apart from others that could never be.

Who would you believe?

I'm not afraid to hold you, I'm not afraid of your thorns.

I'm afraid that if I leave you here, somebody else might see you too.

I want to be the arms you feel safe in.

I want you to be able to trust that these hands of mine will only be here to hold you.

I want you to know my eyes will be the most honest thing about me.

I want you to know my words will only breed life in our conversations.

I want you to know the path that was paved came from God and he orders my footsteps.

I want you to know that when we make love that will be a time when our souls rejoice together.

Know that when times get tough I will be here,
Know that your words matter to me,
Know that I will hear your silence loud and clear.

I want you to allow yourself to be loved again and I want you to trust me when I say that love won't go away this time. The past does not define who we are today for the lord has made all things new and I'm glad God placed you in front of me when he did.

I want to know you like the back of my hand.
I want to know your flaws, your dreams, your failures, your aspirations, the destination to where the key to your heart hides.
I want to know what the silence behind your cries means.
I want to know what's on your mind even if it's nothing so I can plant seeds of imagination creation and self belief in who I already know you to be.

I want to know you, the early morning you, the late night you, the good the bad the ugly
I want you.
I want the you that's afraid to love
I want the you that still has doubts
I want the you that doesn't know if she can trust me or not
I want these things so that God can do what only he can do through me, which is to show you that love still exists in this world.
That you can trust again
That you can love again
That you have something to put your faith in and that's him
I'll be here for the good and the bad but we will get through the storm together

ACT 2

IN MY THOUGHTS

I respect her mind and her body. I cherish her soul, her opinion and her morals. What she says matters to me and how her day goes has become the story I look forward to.

Hearing her voice is the thing that can turn any negative into a positive. Seeing her smile sends a reminder to my heart to skip a beat, but having her by my side is the one thing incomparable to everything else that has ever tried to enter into my life.

The breath of fresh air I breathe in when she smiles in my direction is the thing that reminds me of my purpose in this world which is to love and I will love her.

But what is love?

Love is a contract between two people. Edged in stone by God, something that's patient. Something that's supposed to be so Unbreakable that even if I drop these two stones they'll never crumble because love, it was made by someone who only knew how to give and not ask for any in return.

I want to love you as if I were the only one made for you and only had one chance to give you my all.

You have become the thing that wakes me up at five in the morning just to make sure I didn't miss a call. You have become a part of my daily ritual, almost as if you wrapped yourself in my thoughts, dressed yourself as tomorrow and delivered yourself to me at the perfect time each day.

You make me want to choose you the way I did in my dream
A dream that had many options to choose from but, the one name I could only say was yours, and of course, when I woke it almost had me choked up. With this feeling growing in my chest I thought I was being yoked up by my inner being telling me to show up and let out this contained love that I have for you but in my own head I'm too nervous of a response you haven't given yet so that kept my mouth shut just another day to prolong what is obvious. I'm not proud of this, I'm just scared.

"What do you see?"

Each kiss solidifies the physical agreement we have with each other.

Lip locked, with feelings running towards one another, stumbling over a love neither one of us suspected to find when we found each other.

Her soft skin, her soft gentle hands, digging a grave I'm not afraid to lay in but, scared of what is to become.

Not scared of love, no, scared of what's going to happen if my body hits the ground. Scared of the one thing that's so reckless and dumb, scared of this heart of mine which has cost me love countless times but if you're willing to be mine, I'm fine with falling this time.

And yes I'm still a hopeless romantic, head over heels with candy coated drops of rain easing the pain of this bleeding heart that's been broken once before, twice before, three times maybe four but, after last walked out the door, I thought I was done for sure but, here we are

In the airport Café drinking coffee as I get lost in the flicker of love that grows with each step I take while looking at you.

Silent at times, I know the patience God has given you to sit and pry at the same nail that holds my lips together has to be in abundance because it's a broken one.

I struggle opening fully to the ones that want to know me intimately.

See I've been hurt before stabbed through the chest
I need to be reassured because my words have been leaked before to others by the one I trusted the most and they still beat me for.

So with my secrets out, you can see why I swallowed any key that remained to my words. So thank you for bearing with me but, when will your patience be depleted?

If I needed hours upon hours to sit with you and ponder my thoughts before I let them come out, would you still be there waiting wide eyed hoping for me to invite you into my deepest thoughts or would you pass like the time?

I need you here.

I wonder how I've been blessed with someone as gentle as you, someone who takes the time to hear what's on my mind, doesn't interrupt with what's on hers and helps me get to a resolution.

I won't take your time in vain, however, the pain I've felt left me with a bad hand and with the one I've been dealt, I'm trying to play my cards right, so I beg of you, please don't make me fold.

I'm all in. I'll willingly let you know that as the King's queen, my jack will not be filled with any jokers that are looking to play an ace and kill my Royalty because of a nine so stay close to me and I'll protect us.

You're the ten I got but I still have opponents, I got to play my cards right. At any given night the one to the right might poke her face through my secrets and call my bluff. So can I trust you, I want to but can I? I'm okay with letting you in but will it bite me in the end or will I win? Time will only tell.

ACT 3

THE BREAK

You're the best decision I ever made that cost me the most I never thought I'd be willing to give.

I've come to realize I have a child like love.

And like a child I tend to hold on tight to things that I hold so dear to my heart because I don't know the true harm that hides in this world

Im One that loves carelessly.

One that also has experienced a true heart break.

One that even after having experienced true heartbreak, I'm not afraid to say

I love you anyway.

Shattered beyond a doubt.

Missing you crazy, the thoughts of the times we shared together run through my mind at least two times every hour, that's about 48 times a day.

Leaving me dazed and confused with nothing but questions running through my mind.

What happened?

Leaving the old dog to go find the dry bones, only he knows where they hide.

What happened to us?

Being replaced was never a thought that crossed my mind until you brought up another guy. Someone closer than I but yet I persist on this hunt to have your heart be mine but maybe not.

Lie to me, tell me that you love me until I believe that these aren't just words.

Coming on too strong has been a mistake I've made many times but when you know the competition is vicious you tend to make irrational decisions, and I did.

What did I say?

True words spoken, you showed yourself the door. Looked back with one last look of sorry in your eyes and disappeared with a blink. That left me empty. Recalling what I know, running back to the ones that missed me came easy but in comparison they couldn't equate to you and I left them while looking to efface you for the memories.

What comes next?

You touched me spiritually.

Your tears flooded my earth and killed my humanity. The words you unleashed felt like the sharpest of swords killing even the two of us in the process.

Even though it brought a rainbow out of my chest to let me know you'd never do it again, did it have to happen? Even though we have to start over and recreate what went corrupt, the heart of hearts must be freed from their past iniquities and inequities. You have to be forgiven for your own and I have to be the one that does the forgiving to heal these wounds.

Misguided by my deepest desires, the lord knows my heart. You never understood which led to your departure and arrival to another place that's not mine but yet I love you still.

Will you be back I don't know but if so things must change.

Too weak to live up to your expectations, too immersed by your physique I'm glad you're gone. Embarking in new beginnings I set sail to the great unknown for 40 days and 40 nights, venturing towards a greater tomorrow, one where the pain subsides and my brain realizes that you might not be meant for me.

"Where do you see it?"

Your absence breeds violence in the streets of where many hearts lie.

Running back to my past to get away from you I began to dig a grave too deep to lay in.

Rocked and stoned, you leaving felt like an unbearable death, one I nearly survived.

The truth when heard is what made my stomach turn like my ancestors in that 113 degree heat. Your words knocked me off my feet like Tyson did Frazier but still hope for your return felt eminent, so I believed.

Radio silence from the Lord all because my thoughts sounded like a marching band and drowned out his answers, I started to believe my own doubt. Letting my thoughts become God I soon perceived I was only headed down a rabbit hole that had a snake waiting inside.

The cold months felt like the coldest shoulder you could've ever given me but who would've known that the lack of my lips on yours would give you reason to believe I wasn't man enough to love you.

Too much to handle at times you needed some and that's fine I stepped off, allowing you to see what you were missing only for a season before my greatest moments truly began.

Seeing your growth over time with another was entertaining.

The ups and downs any relationship will go through are bound to happen but, you must've put the same spell on him that's on me because neither one of us can leave you alone but I'm okay without you.

My own growth is unmatched.

You're not my bread and butter but just something I'd like to enjoy on the side like an ice cold drink on a hot sunny day but I know I can last without you while I'm inside.

It's what happens on the outside that makes me believe I need a sip of your thirst quenching waters to ease my longing and desires that I Choose not to get from anyone else.

Your fountain seems to be one many have tried to dip their buckets into but going dry at times, I know you're selective.

So where do I stand?

Out of the ordinary apart from the rest you know I'm the best come lay your head back on my chest. My phone is where you reside when our bodies can't collide, come back to me, it's okay if you cry. I'll be the one to break off all the lies and this time you're actually mine.

There was a lot of good and bad during the good.

My heart still hoped for your return but became desolate as the days passed.

With no attempts in action you came back on your own two feet knocking on my door to be let in.

With my guards up, facing the unknowns, when I saw you, I couldn't remember the time apart. It felt like my past was erased when we reconnected and with no spite detected you wore down my walls, marched in and fell into my arms like I knew you would.

Although I was Overcome with joy by your return, this time was different. This time I was different, not the same guy you knew when you left but part of the best version of myself that I am today.

Walking you around the back gate to be sure not to make the same mistakes I'm glad I could let you back in.

ACT 4

THE RETURN OF LOVE

And the question was asked, Where do you see yourself in five years? My answer, simple, in an airport cafe with the girl of my dreams drinking coffee as I get lost in the flicker of love that grows with each sip I take while I'm looking at her.

Me, I don't want to be another chapter in her story. I want to be the backbone that holds her book together, the thing that protects her sheets, the reason why she feels safe enough to tell her secrets through a pen, and create Something sweet enough to read daily.

I want to travel her mind each night and plant gardens of life so that when she opens her eyes in the morning she can see the beauty in the things that are ugly around her.

Now Her voice serenades my soul with the sweet melodies that spill from her mouth. Her eyes relax me. Her hands make me feel strong. Her lips remind me that I am not alone. And when she asks me to hold her she's in my arms before she can even finish the sentence.

See I've loved this girl before I even opened my mouth to say hello. She's been the girl I prayed for when I was five and has been the one I've been praying for since five in the morning. The one I've been dreaming about before I knew what love was. The one that gave me three chances to prove that I am the one guy that can love her properly.

And as We finish our coffee and my dream becomes a reality once again I'd look at her with love in my eyes and I'd smile.

She'd take my hand, lean over and kiss me and I'd fall in love with her all over again.

And the question was asked, where do you see yourself in five years?

My answer, simple, with you.

"How do you see it?"

I don't care who you talk to throughout the day, as long as I'm the one you're laying next to every night.

What I'm saying is, be my Lois Lane, I'll be your Superman, be the wind underneath my wings; lift me up and let's fight everything that tries to come up and turn us against each other.

You're my kryptonite, my weakness but, I still want you to be my peace, my symbol of hope, the only thing that can bring me to my knees just to make you sound like the angels of heaven when I kiss the places only I can find, And when I penetrate your darkness with the missing key that unlocks the things you hold private, lay down and allow me to love you in a way nobody could ever.

Love me as if I'm one of the only real loves you'll ever experience.

Realize that time together is like the two hands in a clock, bound together forever, seamlessly tied to one another by these chains that hold them in place but sound the alarm to remember that our love lives in eternity.

When our time together ends here on this earth it'll allow us to love one another forever but for now, let's cherish the time that we do have as long as the longest moment will last.

I began to realize that love for you has altered me into a more peaceful man. A man that only allowed his hands to speak for him but when I voiced my emotions I only spoke in violence and destruction.

Your beauty alone has begun to make my heart grow every time it beats to the thought of your smile. I've become more patient and kind. I no longer envy a relationship or boast about my own. I love the way that God intended us to love, the right way.

I like how you see through my cracks.

You know when I'm down and you don't allow me to stay in my own sorrow alone.

You've picked me up out of my darkness and been the light I needed to see the bigger picture.

God put you in front of me and I thank him for that.

But why did you return, what did you see? The potential as I did or did you see the work that God has done in my life?

I want you here but I must be attentive. I have to watch you because although I changed, did you?

Maturity is a rare commodity so would the words of the ones around you be sound canceling to the ones I speak or would you set mine aside and value me more than them or equally?

The last couldn't love you the way you know I can. He was a little boy. I'm a grown man, confident without a doubt I won't give you a reason to scream and shout unless we're making love. So unless you allow me to dip my hand into forever and spark your waters that run deep I won't give you a reason to fight.

Maturity breeds conversation. One thing we couldn't do before but now we know how to work out our issues, you got a problem you run to me the problems stay between A and B because I know that if any outside variable can see the chip in our armor they'll break skin and try to enter into our place and destroy what we've built.

I can make you my queen. I can seat you in high places. I can send my army's to fight the wars we don't have the energy to fight and I can protect your sheets if you allow me to, but the choice is yours.

I prayed for you and God answered with you in return. This love might not come easy but this time love is here to stay.

ACT 5

QUESTIONING MYSELF

Although she trusts me, am I still a stranger in her eyes?

Trying to give way to the truth and out way the lie, I wonder what she really thinks of me.
I wonder if I'm really the last thing on her mind before she falls asleep.
I wonder why God had blessed me with the ability to love her in such a way that no other man could even measure up to.
I wonder if she would let me love her as if it's the only thing I've ever done correctly.
I wonder if my name crosses her mind when a guy introduces himself to her for the first time but I question if I'm just something that's here for now.

A constant battle in my head, trying to decipher whether or not I'm the one God called for her. I don't know but, for what I do know, I know love can't be forced.

You must be willing to allow your heart to be placed in hands that still have a possibility of dropping it but pray to God that they don't.

Can you hear her when she's telling you how to love her?

Are you listening or is your pride too loud to hear her desperate cries for love?

Do you love her or do you love what she can provide?

What do you believe?

Do you actually love her or is the infatuation infectious?

When will you speak up and say what needs to be said with your chest?

Addressing the elephant in the room, there has to be a mutual feeling there, right?

My Persistence gets me in trouble.

I allow my heart to dictate my every action and my brain sends pain signals through my gut to let me know whenever someone walks out the door.

What is real love?

That is something I've been trying to discover over the last few years but, it seems to be the one thing that pushes those so close to falling for it away from me and the rejection kills me.

My past resurrects me from a grave of empty sheets I left wet without giving a second glance to the "here lies another broken heart" sign above the bed and due to my own brokenness, I've left many shattered.

Sometimes it seems like I am the only thing keeping love from finding me. The question now becomes, why be persistent at all?

DO I LOVE MYSELF?

I don't call her what I once did.

As she rips herself from my arms, my heart going with her, me reaching for the last glimpse of hope to recover something so gone I sit and pray to God asking, will she ever be back?

If only she knew how much I loved her, how many hours I prayed for her, how many scars I took trying to change my skin to fit into her closet, if only she knew. Would she love me the way I do her?

Am I enough? Does she see the same future as I or am I color blind to the rose colored glasses that may make red flags appear green? I know my way around words, they make me appear to be better than I am but, are we relishing the moments shared in a lie? I need an answer, hoping my pride doesn't get in the way as it tends to do. You need proof that my heart belongs to you but do you even like me? Subtle things make me question if you do but I pay them no mind because time together feels spaceless, like there is no room for doubt. I question a lot of things due to the lack of my own understanding and trust but leaning not on that, I started to realize that God has ordained this to be. So with mixed emotions stirring, the Lord himself reminds me that he put you here in my life himself, it's up to me to not mess this up because of my fear.

"What do you see now?"

THE BRIDGE

The Voices, louder than ever before "tell her" is all I hear. Each hour that slips, as I beat around the bush with what's truly on my mind, the voice gets louder "Tell her" I can't, as I think to myself, there's no way I can say that to her

"TELL her" no I can't handle the rejection. My heart beating like a drum sweat spewing from everywhere nerves causing my body to rock but the voice ready to roll "TELL HER" me putting up a good fight but too exhausted after the mental anguish I've put myself through, my fear and pride try to suppress what has been boiling in this pot and with my top ready to explode "TELL HER"

I love you.

Three words too quick for me to grab them before they slipped off my lips. The look of shock on her face said it all. Her only question is "What do you love about me?"

ACT 6

THE CONFESSION

Because of my last relationship when it came to you I wanted to give you a stronger perception of who I wasn't so you'd stay around who you saw

For you to understand I have to give you the history. For if I don't, you'll never believe This story

Truth be told, I've been hurt before. The feeling of love was left on the flight I was taking to get back to the first girl that ever tattooed her name on the lockbox of my memory.

I could see her in everything I did. She was the one who made me know it's possible to go above and beyond and be blinded by the light which is the fact that you've never received anything in return.

Heart left shattered on a Friday afternoon, I decided my new mentality would be one that could never be seen through, even if it was a glass house.

No more shattered glass, no more self doubt, no more emotions, I could no longer allow love to be the one that dictated what stayed and what didn't. I decided to make my own decision.

In the process of running away from love, I've pulled the love out of many just for my own satisfaction. So what inevitably broke me broke others and due to the lack of explanation I was gone before they could even ask me "why"

This jar of broken hearts has overflowed to the point where I needed buckets to hold the tears and bloodshed of the massacres I was causing.

Beauties losing their innocence to a man who could chameleon himself to be the guy they always dreamed of having, but could alter his appearance to leave unnoticed. *Attachment was never what I was looking for.* So when tragedy struck, I was nowhere to be found. And with no shoulder to cry on, no truth to be told, and currently heartless, the resentment that began to fester towards me, has bubbled over the fault lines of the names we carved in these rocks that I made them stand on to believe I was the only one made for them.

So if truth be told, I left more shattered due to the instability of what held my heart previously and I have to apologize.

Learning love is still something that I'm doing. I'm learning to love myself so that when it comes to you I can love you exactly how you need to be loved How you should be loved and how you want to be loved but I'm still learning.

In my desperate attempts to be forgiven for my unforgivable I began to
do the unimaginable

Staying true to myself and killing my lies still
This is a test of times and I finally realized
In love you take many scars while not
Losing yourself to be who they want you to be but
Looking to become whole

Leaning no longer on my own understanding
Overcoming my own self doubt
Voicing my love for you feels infeasible with
Everlasting thoughts of us together lingering in my mind every night

Yesterday's mistakes are today's corrections
Ongoing beliefs make me ponder your feelings not just my own because
Understanding you is the key to our longevity

Becoming one is what I truly long for but
Unfolding the truth that hides behind my heart
Trusting that you'll love me for who I am and not hate me for who I was
is the thing that will set you apart from the masses

I Intentionally left my heart at your door

Hoping you'll receive it with open
Arms
Viably believing the definition and
Embracing the unknown unspoken truth of what is to come but having
said that I have

This inevitable feeling that could lead to an
Outcome that might leave our tongues speechless when we both come
clean

Limitless at times I know my tongue best so in times of silence
Embodied In that moment alone knowing that I have let my words spill
like ink many times before
Thinking on times when it came easy to say but this time with these
three words I can't be sure

You've become the blueprint that no other can measure up to
Outlining the things that have caught my eye while keeping me on my
toes you have
Undoubtedly become my favorite reason to work on myself and build a
better foundation

Grant my wish
Open your heart to me and allow me to build on top of the foundation
I have set with you on it

Allow me this one chance
Like no other
To love you although many have tried before
Hang your truth on my cross
Open up to me
Unlock the chambers to the safeguard that protects what you left
unprotected once and
Grant me this wish
Hang on to me and trust that I'll be here to love you in your darkest time

I understand the walls that you've built I've been the cause of many to
be built myself

Still would you believe me if I told you I love you
Think about it
If you Invite me in
Lead me to the private things that no one knows but you
Let me show you why you can trust me and you'll finally see everything
that could be

Words can only get me so far
And with mine I've messed up countless times
Nevertheless my actions can speak for me
Time and time again they've said what my mouth couldn't build the
courage to say so let me prove to you why I love you

Yearning of the
One opportunity to
Undo what I've done to those who came before you but do you trust me?

Hearing what I wanted you to hear has swayed your view on how you
look at me
Enticed by what could be I forgot to look at what it really was
Rigorously repeating the day we met to
Endure the painful thoughts of your absence as if that would ever
meet me

My confidence in my ability to break
You out that shell that keeps you from loving me is outrageous

Daring to do the unthinkable
Ego and high self esteem two things that mixed together to make me
a man with
Ambitious attempts to do things that shouldn't be done
Regrettably it's cost me more than I was ever willing to pay

Without the willingness to say what's needed to be said when it needs
to be said, Will I Endure the fruits of my labor alone?

Misguided emotions lead to my own tyranny
Unjustified heartbreak lead to many of my mistakes
Surrounded by my clouded judgment what sense would it make to
Take what's yours and do to you what's been done to me, I would only
be foolish

Denouncing my past in hopes for a better future
Evidence will only show you the truth
Pleading with a bleeding heart on my sleeve
Apart from these I can finally tell you what I believe
Ratified with the very ink I've spilled on many pages
To say this

Frightened at once of falling I've been very conscious of my decisions
so I'm
Okay with where I am now
Remembering where I was I'm no longer afraid to fall

Ignite my flame, allow me to be the light at the end of the tunnel
Follow me and trust that I won't lead you wrong

Worry not if another has my eye for you are the one that
Enticed me to get close but now I still can't withstand the pain of being
away from you

Stand by me hold me up be the backbone I need to take on this world
Teach me how to respect your mind body and soul
Acclimate your fantasy to my reality and
You will see my work in effect

Together we can be one
Opportunities may rise and they may be better than I
Guessing this will work is the epitome of the moon landing and us
taking our first step towards love is destined to be great
Everyone before couldn't last and anyone after will pass but
True to me I know that nobody can love you like I love you
Humble enough to believe in the love that God gave me but confident
enough to believe what I say is true
Erase past mistakes
Reclaim the thing that was left at your door my heart is yours

With our hearts intertwined for eternity
Everlasting seems to be the realest thing ever

Worrying not about what tomorrow holds because staying in the
moment with you
Is what is important to me
Loving each other until death do us part
Leaves me speechless to the thought

Now thinking that I could actually do this involved my heart to go
through some things
Eradicated my fear of loneliness to see the joint union of us
Variables, there are none
Evidently you get me so with no Epiphany my
Reality involves only us

Looking towards the future while staying in the moment careful to
not be
Overcome with emotions
Valuing your mind just as my own
Everything seems to be great

Another good thing
Not to be
Destroyed by my own doubt

Take my hand
Hold on to it tight
And believe that I'll never let you go
Trust that your heart is safe with me

Where would you want to be
On one side you look at me with love in your eyes
Underlying truths become hard to see without both eyes open
Lay down your guards and
Dance with me in the field of dreams, the dreams we dream together

Our souls are tied together
Nothing can break us apart
Lean on me and I will protect the both of us because
You mean the world to me

Talk to me whenever you're having doubts and I will
Ensure you that I'm not going anywhere
Again I say love me wholeheartedly
Right to left our names on this love will be edged in stone

Unchain yourself from the lies the enemy tried to place in your mind and
See that we are too much for him, them, and anyone to handle

Again I say I love you
Please know it's true
Again I say I love you
Rest assured this story is about you
Thank you for being here, Bryanna, I love you

To those of you who don't feel like you deserve love or that you're not loved, God wants you to know that you are Loved and that you do Deserve to be loved but the right way so I pray that whoever this reaches learns what true love is. Not only that you learn what true love is but that you also get to experience it in a way that I have, which is from God himself. So even if you never experience it from someone else here on earth, I hope that you first love yourself and that the love for yourself stays in your heart so that you'll willingly give it to those who need it. Always remember that God loves you and I do too.

John 15:9

I have loved you even as the Father has loved me. Remain in my love.

1 Corinthians 13:4–8 NLT

4 Love is patient and kind. Love is not jealous or boastful or proud 5 or rude. It does not demand its own way. It is not irritable, and it keeps no record of being wronged. 6 It does not rejoice about injustice but rejoices whenever the truth wins out. 7 Love never gives up, never loses faith, is always hopeful, and endures through every circumstance.
8 Prophecy and speaking in unknown languages [b] and special knowledge will become useless. But love will last forever!

Now I see it

Milton Keynes UK
Ingram Content Group UK Ltd.
UKHW042010201123
432954UK00011B/516/J